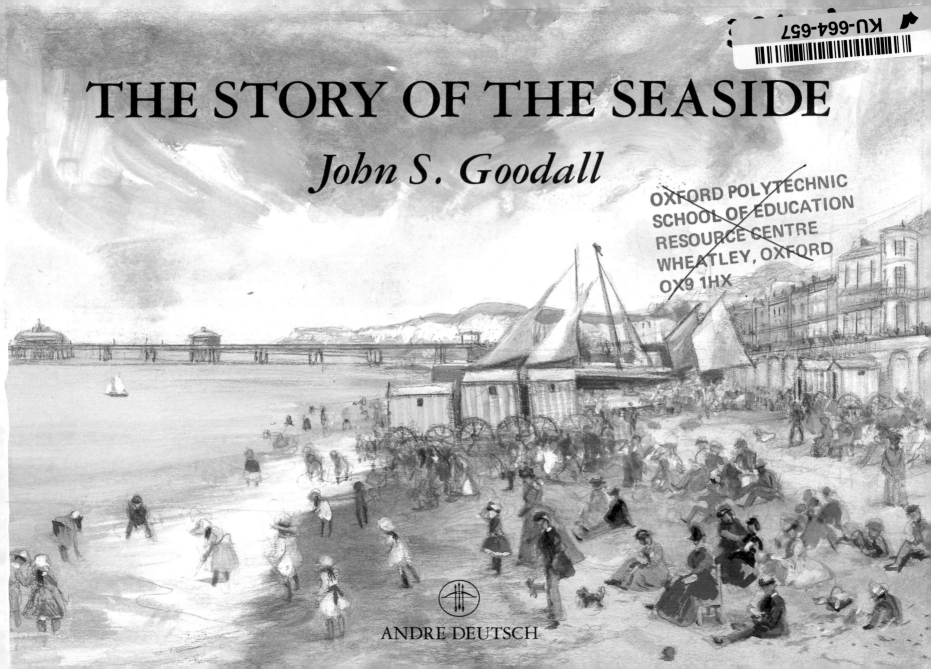

THE STORY OF THE SEASIDE

John S. Goodall

ANDRE DEUTSCH

First published in 1990 by
André Deutsch Limited
105-106 Great Russell Street, London WC1B 3LJ

ISBN 0 233 98422 4

Printed in Hong Kong

In the early 1800s King George III took his family to Weymouth for their health, and so began a fashion for seaside holidays, and the development of the seaside town as a place in which to enjoy yourself, whatever the weather.

5

11

12

13

14

15

DAY
TRIPS
3D

19

DRINKS TEAS REFRESHMENTS

APARTMENTS

BOAT
FOR
HIRE

24

ROOM TO LET

TOYS

HIGH STREET

27

29

MEMB

34

49